REVISE 11+

CW00689183

Also available to support
Verbal Reasoning 11+ revision:

REVISE 11+ — Verbal Reasoning Practice Book 1 — Great preparation for all 11+ exams! — Pearson

REVISE 11+ — Verbal Reasoning Practice Book 2 — Great preparation for all 11+ exams! — Pearson

REVISE 11+ — Verbal Reasoning Assessment Book — Great preparation for all 11+ exams! — Pearson

Verbal Reasoning
Ten-Minute Tests

Series Consultant: Harry Smith
Author: Susan Purcell

THE REVISE 11+ SERIES
For the full range of Pearson Revise 11+ titles visit:
www.pearsonschools.co.uk/revise11plus

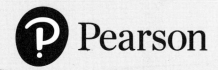

Pearson

Contents

How to use this book

Each test corresponds to a practice section in one of the two Revise 11+ Verbal Reasoning Practice Books.

Work through the practice sections, then have a go at the corresponding Ten-Minute Test.

You could also work through the tests in order, or focus on the skills you know you need more practice in first.

Spend 10 minutes on each test and use the answers in the back of the book to mark your work.

1 Combining words

In vocabulary building questions, you will be asked to combine words to make a new word.

1 Underline **two** words, one in each set of brackets, that can be added together to make another word.

For example: (eye, bird, <u>ear</u>)   (sty, den, <u>nest</u>)

a   (one, any, more)   (day, ever, way)

b   (cap, high, top)   (city, size, ten)

c   (dig, bud, mar)   (end, get, let)

d   (ant, let, wet)   (hem, led, our)

$\boxed{4}$ marks

2 Use a line to join a word on the left with a word on the right to make **four** compound words.

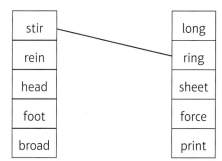

$\boxed{4}$ marks

3 Write **one** word that can be used in front of these words to make four new words.

For example: berry   bell   bottle   print   _____<u>blue</u>_____

a   colour   fall   melon   tight   _____

b   field   line   lock   strip   _____

c   cap   fall   gown   mare   _____

$\boxed{3}$ marks

4 Choose **one** word from the right that makes a new word when added to the word on the left. Underline your answer.

For example: arm   and / full / here / <u>our</u> / sty

a   may   ear / fold / hem / king / post

b   sun   dry / lay / net / shot / side

c   dam   ash / edge / pun / sell / son

$\boxed{3}$ marks

Time to reflect

Mark your test out of 14. How did you do?

Check your answers in the back of the book. If any of your answers are incorrect, go to practice section 1 in Practice Book 1 to revise this topic.

2 Homophones

In homophone questions, you will need to use the meanings of words to recognise their correct spellings.

10

1 Write the correct homophone to complete the sentences.

For example: The yellow part of an egg is called the _____yolk_____ (yoke / yolk).

a In the school orchestra, Sadie plays the _____ (cymbals / symbols).

b We sat and looked at the sea from the _____ (key / quay).

c The pedestrian crossed the street while the traffic was _____ (stationary / stationery).

d You need to _____ (practice / practise) every day if you want to be a professional musician.

4 marks

2 Underline the correct homophone to complete the sentences.

For example: The robbers agreed on an alibi to put the police off the (cent   sent   scent).

a We've had a few (miner   minor   mynah) problems with our new computer system.

b They'll (way   weigh   whey) your parcel at the post office.

c The explosives are enough to (raze   raise   rays) the building to the ground.

3 marks

3 Circle the homophones that have been used **incorrectly** in the passage below.

Dad and I went to the supermarket to bye food for tonight's meal. We bought some flower to make pizza doe, two chilly peppers, some green beans and a few mushrooms. We walked up and down all of the isles looking for tomato source.

5 marks

4 Write the correct homophone to complete the sentences.

For example: The footballer _____passed_____ (passed / past) the ball to another player in his _____team_____ (team / teem).

a Our teacher asked us to _____ (review / revue) the book and discuss the _____ (principal / principle) themes.

b Mum asked me to _____ (peal / peel) some potatoes and _____ (grate / great) some cheese.

c We spotted a small cave at the _____ (base / bass) of the _____ (shear / sheer) cliff.

d You can fish from the _____ (peer / pier) at high _____ (tide / tied).

8 marks

Time to reflect

Mark your test out of 20. How did you do?

Check your answers in the back of the book. If any of your answers are incorrect, go to practice section 2 in Practice Book 1 to revise this topic.

3 Move a letter

In these questions, you take a letter out of one word and insert it into another. You must not rearrange the letters in either word.

1 One letter can be moved from the first word and added to the second word to make two new words. Circle the letter that can be moved.

For example: flute   beret

ⓕ l   u   t   e

a beard   steak

b   e   a   r   d

b clamp   create

c   l   a   m   p

c bread   sale

b   r   e   a   d

3 marks

2 Make new words by adding a letter from the box to each word. Write the new words on the lines. You may use each letter once.

c	o	t	ɇ

For example: cure   _____curve_____

a deer   _____

b meter   _____

c septic   _____

3 marks

3 Move one letter from the word on the left into the word on the right to make two new words. Write the new words on the lines.

For example: carat   horse   _____cart_____   _____hoarse_____

a heaven   fright   _____   _____

b canter   bugle   _____   _____

c pearl   sight   _____   _____

3 marks

4 Move one letter from the first word into the second word to make two new words. Tick the letter that can be moved.

For example: petal   moral   p☐ e☐ t☑ a☐ l☐

a brush   garage   b☐ r☐ u☐ s☐ h☐

b solid   gene   s☐ o☐ l☐ i☐ d☐

c below   grim   b☐ e☐ l☐ o☐ w☐

3 marks

⏱ 10

Time to reflect

Mark your test out of 12. How did you do?

Check your answers in the back of the book. If any of your answers are incorrect, go to practice section 3 in Practice Book 1 to revise this topic.

4 Common letters

With these questions, you often need to add a letter to the beginning or end of one or more words to find completely different words. Sometimes you will be asked to write two letters, at the front and the end of a sequence of letters, to form two different words.

1 Find one letter that can be added to the **beginning** of every word in the set to make new words. Write the letter on the line.

For example: _amp   _raft   _ice   _well   _ream   ___d___

a   _pal   _live   _men   _range   _dour   _____

b   _adder   _hovel   _lime   _train   _tripe   _____

2 marks

2 Write one letter on the line that can be added to the **end** of every word in the set to make new words.

For example: den_   car_   boos_   gran_   flee_   ___t___

a   her_   vet_   came_   lass_   rode_   _____

b   bid_   cub_   mad_   plum_   shin_   _____

2 marks

3 Find the letter which will **end** the first word and **start** the second. Write the letter inside the brackets.

For example: blan [___k___] ettle

a   stra [_____] heat

b   men [_____] nit

c   chin [_____] isle

3 marks

4 Find the letter which will complete **both** pairs of words, **ending** the first word and **starting** the second. Write the letter on the line.

For example: aloo [___f___] irst   snif [___f___] rog

a   leve [_____] arch   scow [_____] odge

b   bell [_____] east   deca [_____] earn

c   his [_____] weat   new [_____] prite

3 marks

5 Find two letters that, together, will **end** the first word and **start** the second word. Write them on the line.

For example: rea [___ch___] air

a   car [_____] ose

b   gra [_____] rch

c   ado [_____] alm

3 marks

10

Time to reflect

Mark your test out of 13. How did you do?

Check your answers in the back of the book. If any of your answers are incorrect, go to practice section 3 in Practice Book 1 to revise this topic.

5 Groups of words

You need to know that words can have different meanings, and what these meanings are. You could be asked to group words which have a similar or related meaning.

1 Underline **one** word that fits with each list of words.

For example: crow, dove, swallow, swift

bird   butterfly   <u>kestrel</u>   moth   penguin

a   noun, adjective, preposition, adverb

verb   tense   grammar   spelling   punctuation

b   cream, milk, butter, cheese

bread   sugar   fruit   yogurt   cereal

c   amber, jade, opal, turquoise

green   ruby   gem   aqua   gold

d   cone, cube, cylinder, cuboid

square   geometry   sphere   triangle   circle

4 marks

2 Underline **one** word in brackets that goes with **both** pairs of words.

For example: allow, permit   rent, hire   (loan, lend, <u>let</u>, license, leash)

a   call, phone   band, circle   (disc, ring, halo, loop, dial)

b   fracture, smash   recess, pause   (rest, interval, crack, break, shatter)

c   current, existing   gift, donation   (award, bonus, topical, present, contribution)

d   biro, ballpoint   cage, pound   (marker, pen, write, coop, enclosure)

e   volume, novel   reserve, order   (book, play, tome, charter, register)

5 marks

3 Underline **one** word outside the brackets that has a similar meaning to the words inside the brackets.

For example: (rod, stick)   (forbid, prohibit)   <u>bar</u>, baton, post, ban, protest

a   (tolerate, endure)   (carry, convey)   bring, hold, bear, suffer, stand

b   (blonde, light)   (just, impartial)   honest, equal, pale, fair, golden

c   (rubbish, garbage)   (decline, reject)   refuse, protest, waste, litter, dismiss

d   (item, thing)   (protest, oppose)   article, issue, mind, complain, object

e   (tailback, congestion)   (preserve, conserve)   line, bottle, jam, stop, obstruct

5 marks

Time to reflect

Mark your test out of 14. How did you do?

Check your answers in the back of the book. If any of your answers are incorrect, go to practice section 5 in Practice Book 1 to revise this topic.

6 Words most similar

In this type of question, you need to know the meanings of words, so that you can recognise two words that mean the same, or nearly the same. Often you will need to spell these words, too.

10

1   Underline the **two** words, one from each set of brackets, that are closest in meaning.

For example: (weep, fatigued, <u>sad</u>)   (discontent, discomfort, <u>melancholy</u>)

a   (dream, tired, yawn)   (sleep, exhaust, drowsy)

b   (high, tower, distance)   (tall, wide, altitude)

c   (enjoy, hobby, leisure)   (pastime, favourite, active)

d   (spectacle, watch, guard)   (observe, time, audience)

e   (straight, right, exactly)   (left, correct, remedy)

f   (pine, tree, extent)   (long, wood, strength)

6 marks

2   Underline the word that is similar in meaning to the word on the left.

For example: ring: around   <u>circle</u>   jewel   finger

a   live: home   breath   energy   dwell

b   detest: hatred   loathe   repel   disgust

c   trick: magic   pretend   cheat   dishonest

d   vain: arrogant   pride   streak   conceited

e   stately: majestic   dignified   ceremony   national

5 marks

3   Complete the word on the right so that it has a similar meaning as the word on the left.

For example: real   g e <u>n</u> <u>u</u> <u>i</u> n e

a   ridiculous   _ b _ _ r d

b   copy   d _ _ l i _ _ t e

c   scared   f e _ _ _ u l

d   need   r e _ _ _ _ r e

e   sick   n _ _ s _ _ u s

5 marks

Time to reflect

Mark your test out of 16. How did you do?

Check your answers in the back of the book. If any of your answers are incorrect, go to practice section 1 in Practice Book 2 to revise this topic.

7 Words most opposite

This type of question asks you to find words that are opposite in meaning, or antonyms. It looks very similar to the 'words most similar' questions, so make sure you read the question carefully.

1   Underline the **two** words, one from each set of brackets, that are most opposite in meaning.

For example: (procure, eat, <u>produce</u>)   (console, <u>consume</u>, sleep)

a   (routine, uniform, contrast)   (varied, boring, attractive)

b   (plain, patchy, smooth)   (hill, pattern, fancy)

c   (descent, incline, raise)   (alight, lower, elevate)

d   (solid, hard, pure)   (lazy, flimsy, robust)

e   (extreme, violent, wild)   (tame, willing, mercy)

f   (liberal, lawful, unruly)   (prohibit, illegal, permissible)

6
marks

2   Underline the word that means the opposite of the word on the left.

For example: dark: lighten   unlit   <u>pale</u>   pitch

a   polite: contempt   insolent   imprudent   esteem

b   fertile: original   barren   desert   feeble

c   naive: sophisticated   guilty   inexperienced   deceit

d   loser: win   triumph   prize   victor

e   arrive: departure   leave   absent   escape

5
marks

3   Complete the word on the right so that it is opposite in meaning to the word on the left.

For example: unlucky   <u>f</u> o r t <u>u n</u> a t e

a   vice   _ _ r t _ e

b   host   _ u e _ _

c   certain   u _ _ u _ e

d   long   b _ _ e _

e   lead   _ o l _ _ w

5
marks

Time to reflect

Mark your test out of 16. How did you do?

Check your answers in the back of the book. If any of your answers are incorrect, go to practice section 2 in Practice Book 2 to revise this topic.

8 Antonyms and synonyms

Here you will be given a set of words and you will be asked to find words in that set that are antonyms or synonyms of another word.

1 Read the words in the grid and then use them to answer the questions that follow.

10

dice	poverty	adult	dismiss	destitute
penny	early	needy	chief	late
interior	principle	prosper	pointless	cut
block	ashes	centre	advance	greedy
sack	ignition	overdue	exterior	explosion

For example: Find and write **one** word that is a **synonym** for the word **main**.   _____ chief _____

a Find and write **two** words that are **antonyms** for the word **wealthy**.

_____   _____

b Find and write **two** words that are **synonyms** for the word **chop**.

_____   _____

c Find and write **one** word that is an **antonym** for the word **inside**.   _____

d Find and write **two** words that are **antonyms** for the word **premature**.

_____   _____

e Find and write **two** words that are **synonyms** for the word **fire**.

_____   _____

9 marks

2 Read the words in the grid and then use them to answer the questions that follow.

undertake	seldom	sightseeing	infrequent	mythology
narrate	usual	amend	refusal	stumble
keep	abundant	extract	nothing	imaginary
altar	reject	meagre	rarely	decline
welcome	story	adjust	unreal	tourism

For example: Find and write **two** words that are **antonyms** for the word **accept**.

_____ reject _____   _____ decline _____

a Find and write **two** words that are **synonyms** for the word **change**.

_____   _____

b Find and write **two** words that are **antonyms** for the word **often**.

_____   _____

c Find and write **one** word that is a **synonym** for the word **trip**.   _____

d Find and write **one** word that is an **antonym** for the word **plentiful**.   _____

e Find and write **two** words that are **synonyms** for the word **fictitious**.

8 marks

_____   _____

Time to reflect

Mark your test out of 17. How did you do?

Check your answers in the back of the book. If any of your answers are incorrect, go to practice section 3 in Practice Book 2 to revise this topic.

9 Anagrams

In anagram questions you will be asked to rearrange the letters to make a word. You will need to be sure of your spelling. When there is a clue, you must pay attention to the meaning of the word.

1 Rearrange the letters to make a word, using the clue to help you. Underline the correct answer.   **10**

For example: RLATE   Clue: an alarm or warning

LATER   APPEAR   <u>ALERT</u>   AWARE

a   ARCTEEL   Clue: thick, black, sticky syrup
NECTAR   CARAMEL   TARMAC   TREACLE

b   TARUINC   Clue: window covering
COTTON   CANOPY   CURTAIN   DRAPE

c   RACETHE   Clue: instructor
TEACHER   TRAINER   TUTOR   LECTURER

d   SPENORES   Clue: a reaction
RESPOND   REPLY   RETORT   RESPONSE

4
marks

2 Rearrange the letters to make a word, using the clue to help you. Write the word on the line.

For example: WESRHO   Clue: rain in April   <u>SHOWER</u>

a   PONLHID   Clue: sea mammal   _____

b   TOPYER   Clue: rhymes and verses   _____

c   OTINUCA   Clue: sale where buyers make bids   _____

d   PONSORIC   Clue: stinging eight-legged creature   _____

e   GIRENUME   Clue: dessert made of egg whites and sugar   _____

5
marks

3 Underline the word or words that **cannot** be made using letters from the first word.

For example: PARACHUTE: CHAPTER   PREACH   <u>THREAT</u>   CHART

a   PRIVATE: TAPER   TRIVIA   PIRATE   PRIVET

b   ISOLATE: LOSER   STALE   STOLEN   TAILS

c   TANGERINE: GREEN   GIANT   THINNER   ENTIRE

d   THEATRE: HEARTH   HEATER   TREAT   RATHER

e   PLATFORM: FARM   MALT   FLAME   MORAL

5
marks

Time to reflect

Mark your test out of 14. How did you do?

Check your answers in the back of the book. If any of your answers are incorrect, go to practice section 4 in Practice Book 2 to revise this topic.

10 Odd words out

These questions rely on your knowledge of the different meanings of words and your understanding of word classes and parts of speech. Decide which word, or which two words, do not belong with the others.

10

1 Underline the **two** words that **do not** belong to the group.

For example: scream   bawl   <u>whisper</u>   yell   <u>sigh</u>

a	lemon	amber	orange	pineapple	lime
b	oil	gas	lead	iron	copper
c	ash	ewe	elm	oak	arc
d	watch	timer	observe	dial	eye

4 marks

2 Three of the words in each list are linked. Circle the word that **does not** belong.

For example: bowler   (batter)   balaclava   bonnet

a	timid	nervous	brash	shy
b	general	common	major	private
c	second	minute	miniature	tiny
d	pound	stone	dollar	euro

4 marks

3 In each of the following sets there is **one** word that **does not** belong. Write the word on the line.

For example: niece   nephew   aunt   ankle   _____ankle_____

a	legend	sequel	fable	myth	_____
b	class	form	shape	mould	_____
c	bus	plane	coach	trainer	_____
d	vixen	ewe	leveret	sow	_____

4 marks

4 Underline the **two** words in each list that **do not** belong.

For example: <u>comply</u>   <u>agree</u>   quarrel   bicker   squabble

a	dash	line	stroll	sprint	race
b	present	gift	flair	shine	talent
c	newt	duck	frog	toad	eel

3 marks

Time to reflect

Mark your test out of 15. How did you do?

Check your answers in the back of the book. If any of your answers are incorrect, go to practice section 6 in Practice Book 1 to revise this topic.

11 Jumbled sentences

These questions test your knowledge of sentence structure. You will need to know the rules concerning word order in English and have a good knowledge of word classes and meanings.

10

1 Underline the **two** words that need to change place for the sentence to make sense.

For example: Matthew ran a hundred <u>seconds</u> in just over ten <u>metres</u>.

a Babysitters look for children after money.

b It's only a loud dog, but it has a small bark.

c I'd like to go see Egypt to to the Pyramids.

d My mum feels boring at work because her job is so frustrated.

e I heard the lion raw when the keeper gave it some roar meat.

5
marks

2 Write the sentences in the correct order.

For example: stay long boat afloat won't for that.

That boat won't stay afloat for long.

a it a match was what fantastic!

_____

b a nightgown was in long she cotton dressed.

_____

c or your miss go better now you'd train you'll.

_____

d went I rather home you would.

_____

4
marks

3 Write the following sentences in the correct order and circle the word that isn't needed.

For example: lion zoo is the(end)a cub of birth the celebrating.

The zoo is celebrating the birth of a lion cub.

a house than the theirs station is ours their nearer.

_____

b all letter I've cousins to my written.

_____

c there have a very is time for to shower me enough?

_____

3
marks

Time to reflect

Mark your test out of 12. How did you do?

Check your answers in the back of the book. If any of your answers are incorrect, go to practice section 7 in Practice Book 1 to revise this topic.

12 Word meanings

These questions test your ability to work out the meaning of a word by understanding the context, or overall meaning, of the sentence. Your knowledge of word classes will help you here too.

10

1 Read the sentence then answer the question. **Underline** the correct answer.

For example: Despite his initial misgivings, Dad agreed to go on a diet.
What does the word **misgivings** mean in this sentence?

shocks   <u>doubts</u>   recipes   losses

a A company needs to attract and retain talented staff.
What does the word **retain** mean in this sentence?
keep   dismiss   remember   recruit

b My taste in music is quite eclectic, ranging from classical to pop.
What does the word **eclectic** mean in this sentence?
fixed   traditional   interesting   varied

c The explorers survived on a meagre diet of fish and berries.
What does the word **meagre** mean in this sentence?
cheap   wholesome   limited   organic

d She lives alone in a ramshackle house with a large untidy garden.
What does the word **ramshackle** mean in this sentence?
small   rickety   sturdy   substantial

4 marks

2 Draw lines to match the words with the correct definitions.

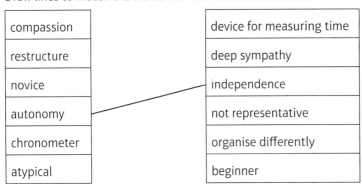

compassion	device for measuring time
restructure	deep sympathy
novice	independence
autonomy	not representative
chronometer	organise differently
atypical	beginner

5 marks

3 Read the sentence and then answer the question.

For example: The living room is airy and spacious, and decorated in warm, <u>inviting</u> tones.
Underline the word in the sentence that means the same as **attractive**.

a Saturn's moon might harbour an underground ocean beneath its icy surface.
Underline the word in the sentence that means the same as **conceal**.

b He is totally charmless, and few people are gullible enough to believe his superficial and glib words.
Underline the word in the sentence that means the same as **trustful**.

c Her candid and uncompromising attitude often annoyed her boss, who was more genial and relaxed.
Underline the word in the sentence that means the same as **inflexible**.

d The children scared their amiable parents by peering through their elaborate, grotesque masks.
Underline the word in the sentence that means the same as **hideous**.

4 marks

Time to reflect

Mark your test out of 13. How did you do?

Check your answers in the back of the book. If any of your answers are incorrect, go to practice section 8 in Practice Book 1 to revise this topic.

13 Word analogies

These questions ask you to spot the relationship between words. This might be to do with meaning, or it might be to do with the spelling or structure of the words.

1 Complete the third pair of words in the same way as the first two pairs. Write the missing word on the line. **10**

For example: (MEDAL   MEAL)   (CREAM   CRAM)   (STAIR ___STIR___)

a (LAND   LEND)   (PARK   PERK)   (RAIN   _____)

b (CARVE   CARE)   (GRIND   GRID)   (COPSE   _____)

c (WORRY   SORRY)   (TABLE   SABLE)   (CANDY   _____)

d (SANG   SNAG)   (BOLT   BLOT)   (FROM   _____)

e (NASTY   TASTY)   (TRIBE   BRIBE)   (FLOCK   _____)

f (PETAL   PEAL)   (RAPID   RAID)   (TIMER   _____)

g (CLOSET   LOSE)   (COVERT   OVER)   (PLENTY   _____)

h (BRAIN   BARN)   (FROCK   FORK)   (PLATE   _____)

i (ARMOUR   HARM)   (EATING   HEAT)   (ALLOWS   _____)

j (LEAF   FLEA)   (EARN   NEAR)   (PANS   _____)

k (BREAD   BUTTER)   (NEEDLE   THREAD)   (THUNDER _____)

l (MORE   LESS)   (TOP   BOTTOM)   (FIRST   _____)

12
marks

2 Look at the groups of words below. Decide which group the words in the questions fit into and write the letter on the line. Use each group once.

A	B	C	~~D~~	E
llama	day	cellar	jump	sandal
donkey	month	crypt	leap	slipper
camel	year	basement	bound	clog

For example: spring   __D__

a week   _____

b mule   _____

c vault   _____

d horse   _____

4
marks

Time to reflect

Mark your test out of 16. How did you do?

Check your answers in the back of the book. If any of your answers are incorrect, go to practice section 5 in Practice Book 2 to revise this topic.

14 Words in context

This type of question asks you to choose words to fit the sense and context of a sentence.

10

1   Complete the sentences by selecting the most sensible word from inside the brackets.
Underline the words selected.
For example: On Saturday we (was, where, <u>are</u>) going to a concert.

   a   The jockey jumped on the (car, ground, horse) and (walked, galloped, grabbed) quickly to the starting line.

   b   My friend Noah is very (kind, mean, spoilt) and likes (talking, giving, helping) people.

   c   We made a (detour, journey, shortcut) in order to (avoid, reduce, prevent) the roadworks on the motorway.

   d   The steak (prepared, rustled, sizzled) in the frying pan and (cooked, reeked, smelled) delicious.

   e   My grandmother (bequeathed, bereaved, requested) £5000 in her (home, testimony, will) to charity.

   f   The wheel of my (car, bicycle, skates) has got a (tyre, lock, puncture) and I can't ride it.

   g   Please (forgive, remind, excuse) me to (buy, post, give) this letter, in case I (remember, forget, go).

   h   There weren't enough (seats, people, opportunities) for everyone in the (furniture, audience, spectators), and some people had to (pretend, sit, stand).

   i   I've eaten far too (many, small, few) peanuts, and have (attacked, relieved, spoilt) my (digest, appetite, hunger).

   j   The (tenants, residences, licences) were given (lease, contract, notice) to leave and (moved, resigned, vacated) the flat last week.

   k   His (income, expenditure, rent) was not (economic, large, lower) enough, and the bank refused him (payment, credit, debit).

   l   During the (ship, sail, cruise) a passenger fell (down, off, overboard) and (drowned, swam, saved).

12
marks

2   Change one word so that the sentences make sense. Draw a line through the word you are replacing and write your new word on the line.
For example: Mum removed the splinter from my finger with her ~~shears~~.   <u>tweezers</u>

   a   They worked in the fields all day from night to dusk.   _____

   b   Don't hear a noise! The baby's asleep.   _____

   c   Granny took up her wool and sticks and began to knit.   _____

   d   The curry isn't bland enough; it needs more chilli.   _____

   e   The bird carried small twigs to the tree to build a cage.   _____

5
marks

Time to reflect

Mark your test out of 17. How did you do?

Check your answers in the back of the book. If any of your answers are incorrect, go to practice section 6 in Practice Book 2 to revise this topic.

15 Complete the sentence

You need to be able to complete single sentences or short paragraphs with missing words. This type of question tests your vocabulary, grammatical knowledge and ability to use context clues.

1 Complete each sentence by filling in the missing letters. **10**

For example: My dog ret _r_ _i_ _e_ _v_ ed the ball from the water and brought it back to me.

a I always ce __ __ __ __ ate my birthday with my family.

b Helicopters ho __ __ __ __ d overhead, surveying the scene.

c The employee was sacked for his outr __ __ __ __ us behaviour.

d A cheetah is so fast that it can o __ __ __ __ n a car.

e Atte __ __ __ __ ce at the meeting is compulsory.

f We should all eat a he __ __ __ __ y diet and take plenty of exercise.

6 marks

2 Write one word to complete each sentence so that it makes sense.

For example: I really __ought__ to visit my grandma at the weekend.
should   can't   ~~ought~~   must   will

a I don't feel well; I think I'm coming _____ with a cold.
up   down   in   along   on

b We went to the park _____ though it was raining.
and   when   even   still   but

c Tom is almost as tall _____ his brother.
as   than   like   to   with

d Mum _____ the baby in her cot and tiptoed away.
lay   laid   lied   lain   lying

e The nurse became _____ worried about the patient's health.
increase   increases   increased   increasing   increasingly

f The train leaves _____ ten minutes from Platform 4.
in   before   during   until   at

6 marks

3 Underline the most appropriate word from the brackets to complete each sentence.

For example: I went to bed early (although, <u>because</u>, whereas, however) I was tired.

a This has been the most difficult (job, role, decision, verdict) I've ever had to make.

b Nobody wanted to (say, tell, remember, advice) the teacher that the clock was fast.

c There were (ever, far, so, such) many mistakes in my maths homework.

d The protestors feel very (highly, powerfully, certainly, strongly) about the issue.

e We had to (cancel, postpone, reserve, advance) our trip to Spain until later in the year.

f My cousins and I went for a leisurely (march, slog, stroll, trek) along the beach.

6 marks

Time to reflect

Mark your test out of 18. How did you do?

Check your answers in the back of the book. If any of your answers are incorrect, go to practice section 7 in Practice Book 2 to revise this topic.

16 Complete the paragraph

In these questions you must fill in multiple missing words in a piece of text. You will need to understand the context of the text, and be able to recognise grammatical clues within individual sentences, in order to find the correct answers.

10

1 Underline the most appropriate word from each set of brackets to complete the passage.
One has been done for you.

The mystery of the Bermuda Triangle has (already, recently, <u>long</u>, still) fascinated the general public. In 1918, a large ship, the USS Cyclops, and its (crew, department, captain, squad) of three hundred men disappeared in this (area, district, place, scene) of the North Atlantic Ocean. In later years, aircraft, too, seemingly vanished without (exception, delay, signs, trace). Some people (prove, claim, calculate, convince) that the disappearances are due to supernatural forces, and may even be linked to the (aged, medieval, mystified, mythical) lost continent of Atlantis. Scientists and (cosmologists, pharmacists, meteorologists, zoologists) say that the region is prone to violent and sudden hurricanes, and is influenced by the Gulf Stream, a strong (current, flood, trickle, overflow), which can carry away debris quickly, making it look as if ships and planes 'disappear'. It is worth remembering that this section of the North Atlantic Ocean is a very busy shipping (line, road, direction, route), with thousands of vessels passing through every year without (incident, precedent, event, encounter).

9
marks

2 Complete the passage by selecting the correct words from the box and writing them on the lines in the passage. Use each word only once. One has been done for you.

| discourages long high often standstill ~~many~~ congestion never heavy gridlocked |

Most big cities were built _____ **many** _____ centuries before the invention of the motor car. This is why we see _____ queues of traffic in town centres, and can _____ find a parking space. Some city centres are almost permanently _____ during the day. Other cities experience heavy _____ during the morning and evening peak hours, with the result that traffic is frequently at a _____ . There are even more serious problems caused by the _____ volume of traffic, however. Studies have proved that exhaust fumes are harmful to human health as well as to the environment. Buses and other forms of public transport might be seen as the solution to the problems, but buses move slowly through _____ traffic, and public transport is _____ expensive, which _____ commuters from using it.

9
marks

Time to reflect

Mark your test out of 18. How did you do?

Check your answers in the back of the book. If any of your answers are incorrect, go to practice section 8 in Practice Book 2 to revise this topic.

17 Completing equations

In these questions, the calculations on either side of the = sign have the same answer. You have to find the missing number.

1   Solve the calculation on the left to find the missing number on the right. Write the answer on the line.

For example: $7 + 4 = 2 + \underline{\quad 9 \quad}$

a $27 + 8 = 5 \times \underline{\qquad}$

b $9 \times 3 = 54 \div \underline{\qquad}$

c $96 \div 8 = 19 - \underline{\qquad}$

d $17 \times 3 = 102 \div \underline{\qquad}$

4
marks

2   Solve the calculation on the right to find the missing number on the left. Write the answer on the line.

For example: $7 \times \underline{\quad 1 \quad} = 21 \div 3$

a $21 - \underline{\qquad} = 39 \div 3$

b $\underline{\qquad} \times 3 = 17 + 4$

c $41 - \underline{\qquad} = 8 \times 4$

d $\underline{\qquad} \div 2 = 20 \times 6$

4
marks

3   Find the missing number in each equation. Circle the correct answer.

For example: $54 - (16 \times 2) = 13 + (3 \times \underline{\qquad})$ (11   7   5   ③   13)

a $2 \times 4 + 3 = \underline{\qquad} - 6$ (17   23   29   31   41)

b $101 - 16 - 8 = 6 \times 8 + \underline{\qquad}$ (27   29   33   37   45)

c $64 \div 8 + 4 = 6 \times 3 - \underline{\qquad}$ (6   8   10   12   16)

d $9 \times 4 \div 6 + 1 = \underline{\qquad} \times 3 - 8$ (5   9   10   11   13)

e $13 \times 5 - 17 = 200 - \underline{\qquad}$ (175   163   152   148   138)

f $(11 \times 10) \div 2 = 36 + \underline{\qquad}$ (12   15   19   20   24)

g $4^2 + 7^2 = 100 - \underline{\qquad}$ (24   35   46   53   65)

h $(40 \div 4) \times 5 = 3000 \div \underline{\qquad}$ (80   60   50   40   20)

8
marks

Time to reflect

Mark your test out of 16. How did you do?

Check your answers in the back of the book. If any of your answers are incorrect, go to practice section 9 in Practice Book 1 to revise this topic.

18 Number analogies

Number analogy questions require logic, deduction and mental arithmetic skills. The challenge is to find the relationship between the numbers in each set and then apply the same rule to identify a missing number.

10

1 Find the relationship between the first two pairs of numbers and apply this to the last pair. Write the missing number on the line.

For example: (3 is to 12)   (4 is to 16)   (5 is to __20__)

a (42 is to 33)   (35 is to 26)   (29 is to _____)

b (17 is to 22)   (26 is to 31)   (35 is to _____)

c (96 is to 8)   (60 is to 5)   (24 is to _____)

d (10 is to 100)   (11 is to 121)   (12 is to _____)

4 marks

2 Find the rule which relates the two numbers outside the bracket to the number inside the bracket. Write the rule in words.

For example: 4 [24] 6   7 [56] 8   The rule is: __*multiply the numbers together.*__

a 3 [14] 4   8 [34] 9   The rule is: _____

b 48 [12] 4   68 [17] 4   The rule is: _____

c 7 [52] 3   8 [69] 5   The rule is: _____

3 marks

3 Find the number that completes the third set of numbers in the same way as the first two sets. Circle the correct answer.

For example: 45 [57] 12   16 [54] 38   78 [?] 17   75   85   ⑨⑤   105   120

a 14 [2] 7   28 [7] 4   18 [?] 6   2   3   4   5   6

b 3 [12] 2   4 [16] 2   4 [?] 7   18   20   27   48   56

c 7 [13] 3   5 [16] 8   8 [?] 9   19   20   30   36   42

d 5 [30] 15   15 [50] 25   45 [?] 75   100   110   120   130   140

4 marks

4 Find the number that completes the third set of numbers in the same way as the first two sets. Write the missing number on the line.

For example: 14 [20] 6   22 [29] 7   24 [__32__] 8

a 7 [6] 5   8 [6] 4   7 [_____] 9

b 15 [18] 6   20 [31] 14   27 [_____] 11

c 2 [15] 3   3 [21] 4   5 [_____] 6

d 7 [13] 3   9 [19] 5   8 [_____] 2

4 marks

Time to reflect

Mark your test out of 15. How did you do?

Check your answers in the back of the book. If any of your answers are incorrect, go to practice section 10 in Practice Book 1 to revise this topic.

19 Algebra

In algebra questions you will be asked to substitute numbers for letters when calculating answers. With these questions you need to think logically and work methodically.

1 If A = 2, B = 3, C = 6, D = 8 and E = 12, what is the value of the following? Write your answer as a letter.

For example: (B × C) – C = ___E___

a (E ÷ B) + D = _____

b AE ÷ B = _____

c C + D – E = _____

d 4B – C = _____

4 marks

2 For E = 1, H = 2, I = 3, L = 4, R = 5, S = 6, T = 7 and W = 8, find the sum when the letters in the following words are added together. Write your answer as a number.

For example: SWELTER = ___32___

a SHELL = _____

b WHISTLE = _____

c RELISH = _____

d TERRIER = _____

4 marks

3 For A = 10, B = 8, C = 5, D = 3 and E = 2, find the value of the following calculations.
Write your answer as a number.

For example: (C × E) + (A – D) = ___17___

a A – D + B = _____

b BE – CD = _____

c AD – B + E = _____

d A + 4D – (B ÷ E) = _____

4 marks

4 Use the information given to answer each sum. Write your answer as a letter.

For example: A = 9, B = 20, C = 72, D = 18, E = 12   C ÷ A + E = ___B___

a A = 40, B = 30, C = 50, D = 20, E = 60   A + C – E = _____

b A = 10, B = 40, C = 5, D = 20, E = 8   CE – D = _____

c A = 24, B = 30, C = 3, D = 6, E = 12   (A + E) ÷ D = _____

d A = 48, B = 32, C = 16, D = 8, E = 4   4B ÷ D = _____

4 marks

Time to reflect

Mark your test out of 16. How did you do?

Check your answers in the back of the book. If any of your answers are incorrect, go to practice section 9 in
Practice Book 2 to revise this topic.

20 Number triples

In this type of question you need to identify the common relationship between two sets of numbers (two or three numbers per set). You must then apply the same relationship to a third set of numbers, where one number is missing.

10

1 The middle numbers are related to the two numbers on either side of them in the same way.
Find and write the missing number on the line

For example: 45 [57] 12   16 [54] 38   78 [?] 17   _____95_____

a   12 [4] 3   20 [5] 4   22 [?] 11   _____

b   5 [24] 7   8 [38] 11   9 [?] 14   _____

c   13 [52] 4   14 [84] 6   16 [?] 8   _____

d   8 [19] 3   6 [20] 8   3 [?] 5   _____

e   4 [30] 10   5 [45] 11   6 [?] 9   _____

f   5 [10] 13   9 [14] 21   8 [?] 27   _____

g   5 [12] 4   3 [10] 6   4 [?] 7   _____

h   24 [11] 2   36 [8] 4   42 [?] 6   _____

8 marks

2 Find the relationship between the first two pairs of numbers and apply this to the last pair to find the missing number. Write the missing number on the line.

For example: (3 is to 12)   (4 is to 16)   (5 is to ?)   _____20_____

a   (4 is to 6.5)   (13.5 is to 16)   (17 is to ?)   _____

b   (5 is to 25)   (7 is to 49)   (9 is to ?)   _____

c   (0.5 is to 0.25)   (1.4 is to 0.7)   (1.9 is to ?)   _____

d   (9 is to 55)   (6 is to 40)   (2 is to ?)   _____

e   (8 is to 88)   (11 is to 121)   (13 is to ?)   _____

f   (512 is to 8)   (216 is to 6)   (125 is to ?)   _____

g   (4 is to 14)   (7 is to 23)   (9 is to ?)   _____

h   (13 is to 6)   (12 is to 5.5)   (9 is to ?)   _____

8 marks

Time to reflect

Mark your test out of 16. How did you do?

Check your answers in the back of the book. If any of your answers are incorrect, go to practice section 10 in Practice Book 1 to revise this topic.

21 Letter sequences

In these questions, you are given a series of letters and asked to find and write the next letters in the sequence. The questions test your ability to find patterns.

1 Write the missing letters to complete the sequence. Use the alphabet to help you. **(10)**

A B C D E F G H I J K L M N O P Q R S T U V W X Y Z

For example: X   V   T   R   P   <u>N</u>   <u>L</u>

a B   A   F   E   J   I   N   ____ ____

b Z   Y   W   T   P   ____ ____

c J   M   P   S   ____ ____

d M   C   N   D   O   E   P   ____ ____

8 marks

2 Write the missing pairs of letters to complete the sequence. Use the alphabet to help you.

A B C D E F G H I J K L M N O P Q R S T U V W X Y Z

For example: BE is to HK as DG is to   <u>JM</u>

a   HQ is to GP as KE is to _____

b   SH is to OL as MN is to _____

c   MK is to NJ as TV is to _____

d   AC is to VW as LB is to _____

4 marks

3 Write the missing pairs of letters to complete the sequence. Use the alphabet to help you.

A B C D E F G H I J K L M N O P Q R S T U V W X Y Z

For example: <u>FS</u>   GU   HW   IY   <u>JA</u>

a NO   PQ   RS   TU   ____ ____

b WV   UT   SR   QP   ____ ____

c KA   NC   QE   TG   ____ ____

d PQ   ST   ____ YZ   BC   ____

e VF   TH   ____ PL   ____ LP

10 marks

[Test continues on the next page]

4 Write the missing letters or pairs of letters to complete the sequence. Use the alphabet to help you.

A B C D E F G H I J K L M N O P Q R S T U V W X Y Z

For example: X   V   T   R   P   <u>N</u>   <u>L</u>

a A   A   C   C   E   E   G   ____   ____

b W   T   Q   N   ____   ____

c MY   OW   QU   SS   ____   ____

d PC   ND   LE   JF   ____   ____

8 marks

Time to reflect

Mark your test out of 30. How did you do?

Check your answers in the back of the book. If any of your answers are incorrect, go to practice section 11 in Practice Book 1 to revise this topic.

22 Number sequences

This type of question gives a series of numbers and asks you to identify the pattern and find the missing numbers in the sequence. It tests your ability to use the four basic arithmetic operations, as well as testing your analysis skills and your ability to spot patterns.

1 Write the missing numbers in the sequence.   **(10)**

For example: 2   5   8   11   14   _17_   _20_

a   1   2   3   5   8   ____ ____

b   9   10.5   12   13.5   15   ____ ____

c   4   10   22   46   94   190   ____ ____

d   12   6   25   12   38   18   ____ ____

e   4   6   ____   16   24   ____   46

f   729   243   81   ____   ____   3

g   1.5   5   12   26   ____   110   ____

14
marks

2 These sequences are complete. Write the rule.

For example: 14   21   28   35   42   49   56   The rule is: _+7_

a   6   24   12   12   24   6   The rule is: _____

b   12   15   24   30   36   45   The rule is: _____

c   80   72   63   53   42   30   The rule is: _____

d   480   240   120   60   30   15   The rule is: _____

e   39   36   31   12   23   4   The rule is: _____

f   7   19   32   46   61   77   The rule is: _____

g   18   21   25   30   36   43   The rule is: _____

7
marks

[Test continues on the next page]

3 Circle the next number in the sequence.

For example: 2   4   8   16   32   64   (88   102   112   (128)   144)

a   3   5   8   13   21   34   (43   55   58   62   66)

b   5   12   19   26   33   40   (45   47   51   54   63)

c   80   25   71   28   62   31   (34   40   45   53   58)

Time to reflect

Mark your test out of 24. How did you do?

Check your answers in the back of the book. If any of your answers are incorrect, go to practice section 12 in Practice Book 1 to revise this topic.

23 Codes and decodes

Code and decode questions test your ability to spot connections and work methodically. Identify the relationship between letters, word and codes, then apply that relationship to find the answer.

1 Each question uses a different code. Use the alphabet to help you work out the answer and write the correct code on the line.

A B C D E F G H I J K L M N O P Q R S T U V W X Y Z

For example: If the code for GOAT is IQCV, what is the code for SHEEP? ___UJGGR___

 a If the code for BLUE is DNWG, what is the code for PINK? _____

 b If MLHV is the code for NOSE, what is the code for FACE? _____

 c If the code for TREE is SQDD, what is the code for BUSH? _____

3 marks

2 Each question uses a different code. Use the alphabet to help you work out the answer and write the correct word on the line.

A B C D E F G H I J K L M N O P Q R S T U V W X Y Z

For example: If the code for FILM is GKOQ, what word has the code NQYMJ? ___MOVIE___

 a If the code for SPEED is WTIIH, what word has the code PMQMX? _____

 b If the code for HERON is EBOLK, what word has the code PQLOH? _____

 c If the code for CHIPS is DGJOT, what word has the code GHTG? _____

3 marks

3 Given that ⌂♦⬤■✓✾♦♦➤ is the code for ORCHESTRA, write the words for the following codes.

For example: ⬤♦✓➤♦✓ ___CREATE___

 a ⬤➤✾♦ _____

 b ✾♦⌂♦✓ _____

 c ⬤■✓➤♦ _____

3 marks

[Test continues on the next page]

4 Each question uses a different code. Use the alphabet to help you work out the answer and write the correct code on the line.

A B C D E F G H I J K L M N O P Q R S T U V W X Y Z

a If the code for BLACK is CNBEL, what is the code for WHITE? _____

b If DPSGR is the code for FRUIT, what is the code for JUICE? _____

c If the code for BREAD is EQHZG, what is the code for BUTTER? _____

d If the code for SCHOOL is VFKRRO, what is the code for DINNER? _____

4
marks

5 Each question uses a different code. Use the alphabet to help you work out the answer and write the correct word on the line.

A B C D E F G H I J K L M N O P Q R S T U V W X Y Z

a If the code for TANGO is GZMTL, what word has the code DZOGA? _____

b If the code for SANDY is RYK7T, what word has the code ACXYC? _____

c If the code for SUMMER is UTOLGQ, what word has the code YHPSGQ? _____

d If the code for SUGAR is HFTZI, what word has the code HKRXV? _____

4
marks

Time to reflect

Mark your test out of 17. How did you do?

Check your answers in the back of the book. If any of your answers are incorrect, go to practice section 13 in Practice Book 1 to revise this topic.

24 Word ladders

In these questions you are asked to change one word into another word, by changing one letter at a time. Each change must result in a new, real word. These questions test your skills of logic and knowledge of spelling.

1 Change the first word into the last word by changing one letter at a time and making **one** new word in the middle.

For example: STOP   ____SLOP____   SLAP

a	BRAG	_____	DRAW
b	HIGH	_____	SIGN
c	PALE	_____	CALM
d	SHOE	_____	CHOP
e	FLOW	_____	BLOT
f	BLUE	_____	GLEE
g	PIER	_____	DEER
h	CAME	_____	HOME
i	LINK	_____	LUCK
j	LEND	_____	MENU

10 marks

2 Change the first word into the last word by changing one letter at a time and making **two** new words in the middle.

For example: SLIM   ____SLAM____   ____SLAY____   PLAY

a	PARK	_____	_____	PINT
b	TWIN	_____	_____	SHUN
c	LOUD	_____	_____	FORM
d	NAIL	_____	_____	WELL
e	PAIR	_____	_____	REIN
f	TREE	_____	_____	FLEA
g	GOOD	_____	_____	FOIL
h	SAIL	_____	_____	RUIN
i	WHALE	_____	_____	THOSE
j	DRINK	_____	_____	BLANK

10 marks

Time to reflect

Mark your test out of 20. How did you do?

Check your answers in the back of the book. If any of your answers are incorrect, go to practice section 11 in Practice Book 2 to revise this topic.

25 Word triples

Here you are asked to identify the pattern that has been used to create a new word out of two other words. You must then apply the same pattern to another set of words to identify and write the third missing word.

10

1   The middle word in the first set of three has been made from letters taken from the other two words in the set. Identify which letters were used to make it and apply the same pattern to the second set to make a new word.

For example: WET (TOE) OAR   HIS (_____SKI_____) KEY

a   SAY (YES) SEE   NOT (_____) HER

b   ALL (LOT) OUT   TOP (_____) INN

c   WAY (WIG) PIG   RUN (_____) BED

d   SAY (GAS) EGG   BOY (_____) ASK

e   MAY (ART) TRY   BEE (_____) FLY

f   PLUM (PLUG) GOOD   SLIM (_____) PALE

g   ROCK (RANK) BAND   PELT (_____) CORK

h   TASK (SKIM) FIRM   ACHE (_____) SLOP

i   WEST (EAST) AREA   BOTH (_____) SAGA

j   STRAW (MARSH) CHARM REALM (_____) ENEMY

k   DRIVE (ROAD) FLOAT   ERROR (_____) ADULT

l   BULKY (MURKY) RUMBA OWNER (_____) TAWNY

m   BELOW (POWER) PEARL TABLE (_____) CHANT

n   MATCH (CREAM) BERRY TRUST (_____) SILKY

14 marks

Time to reflect

Mark your test out of 14. How did you do?

Check your answers in the back of the book. If any of your answers are incorrect, go to practice section 12 in Practice Book 2 to revise this topic.

26 Codes and decodes

In these questions, you are given words and number codes and asked to find the link between them. You might need to write a code for a word, or match the codes to words.

1 Match each word to its code. Write your answers on the lines.

POEM	POET	MOPE	MEET
9665	8769	9786	8765

For example: POEM ___8769___

a POET _____

b MOPE _____

c MEET _____

3 marks

2 Match the number codes to the words. One code is missing. Write your answers on the lines.

BANK	BIRD	KNOB	DRAB
	3592	2973	8463

For example: What is the code for BIRD? ___3592___

a What is the code for BANK? _____

b What does the code 29548 mean? _____

c What does the code 39754 mean? _____

d What is the code for BORN? _____

4 marks

3 Match each word to its code. Write your answers on the lines.

RATS	STAR	PAST	TRAP
5986	8697	6795	7968

For example: RATS ___7968___

a STAR _____

b PAST _____

c TRAP _____

3 marks

⏱ **10**

Time to reflect

Mark your test out of 10. How did you do?

Check your answers in the back of the book. If any of your answers are incorrect, go to practice section 11 in Practice Book 2 to revise this topic.

27 Missing 3 letters

In these questions, you are asked to find three missing letters to complete a word. Sometimes the word is in a sentence, so you need to understand the context. In other exercises there is no context, so you must rely on your knowledge of spelling.

10

1 Circle the three-letter word that completes the word in capital letters.

For example: We filled the garden with beautiful PLS. ROW / (ANT) / EEL

a We took a shorter RE home. ACT / EVE / OUT

b We ELY managed to catch the train in time. BAR / FIN / EAR

c I've got a PLE on my nose. RIP / IMP / TOP

d The company is launching a new SCE to help local schools. ARE / RAP / HEM

4 marks

2 Draw lines to match the words to the letters that are missing. One has been done for you

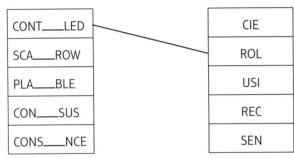

CONT___LED	CIE
SCA___ROW	ROL
PLA___BLE	USI
CON___SUS	REC
CONS___NCE	SEN

4 marks

3 Write the three-letter word that can be added to the letters in capitals to form a complete new word.

For example: We cannot finish the project without the proper RESCES. _____OUR_____

a The soup was watery and MOVER it tasted horrible. _____

b I'm hoping to go to COLE when I finish school. _____

c The DUION of the flight depends on the weather. _____

3 marks

4 Complete the words by writing the three missing letters.

For example: REST _____AUR_____ ANT

a DEF _____ TELY

b AV _____ GE

c BROC _____ I

d PROF _____ OR

4 marks

Time to reflect

Mark your test out of 15. How did you do?

Check your answers in the back of the book. If any of your answers are incorrect, go to practice section 14 in Practice Book 1 to revise this topic.

28 Missing random letters

In these questions, you will be asked to find the missing letters to complete a word, often within a sentence. These questions rely on your comprehension of the context and on your spelling and vocabulary knowledge.

1 Complete the words in the sentences by identifying the missing vowel letters. **(10)**
Write the whole word on the line.

For example: The hotel balcony offers a breathtaking PNRM of the Alps.   ___PANORAMA___

a Eleanor is hard-working and very STDS and always gets good marks.   _____

b There was just one LFGRD on duty at the beach.   _____

c The students have their own bedrooms but share a CMMNL bathroom and kitchen.   _____

d There is free live music every Sunday THRGHT the summer.   _____

e George gave a FCTL account of the week's events.   _____

5 marks

2 Complete the words in the passage by writing the missing letters on the lines.

Conkers is a tra __ __ __ __ onal children's game played with the hard, shiny seeds of horse c __ __ st __ __ t trees.

Two players each use a conker t __ __ __ __ded on to a length of string, and the aim of the game is to smash the

other player's conker to bits. Adults play, too, and there are even co __ __ __ __ itions and a world championship.

These are always held in __ __ tu __ __, which is when conkers fall from the tree. Participants are supplied with

ready-strung conkers – they are not __ __ lo __ ed to use their own, in case they have baked them or soaked them

in vinegar to harden the conker and so obtain an unfair ad __ __ __ __ age over their op __ __ ne __ __. The best

conkers last se__ __ __ __ l seasons and may even be passed down from older to younger si __ __ i __ __ s.

10 marks

3 Complete the words by identifying the missing letters. Use the definitions to help you.
Write the whole word on the line.

For example: VO __ __ AN __ : mountain that erupts hot lava   ___VOLCANO___

a __ UG __ T __ __ E: a person on the run from the police   _____

b AG __ __ ES __ __ VE: ready to attack or start a fight   _____

c CON __ __ AD __ __ T: disagree by saying the opposite   _____

d DE __ __ __ ION: love and loyalty   _____

e DISI __ __ __ __ RATE: crumble or break up into small pieces   _____

f PE __ __ E __ __ AL: lasting forever   _____

6 marks

Time to reflect

Mark your test out of 21. How did you do?

Check your answers in the back of the book. If any of your answers are incorrect, go to practice section 14 in Practice Book 2 to revise this topic.

29 Hidden words

You need to find a four-letter word that is hidden across two or three words in each sentence. Work methodically and check that you know the correct spelling of words.

10

1 Find the four-letter word hidden at the end of one word and the beginning of the next. Underline the word and write it on the line.

For example: Buy whate<u>ver y</u>ou want.   _____very_____

a The bridge needed repair.   _____

b The elephant roared in anger.   _____

c My pyjamas shrank in the wash.   _____

d We went on a coach excursion.   _____

4 marks

2 Find the four-letter word hidden across two consecutive words. Circle the pair of words that contain the hidden word.

For example: Their grammar knowledge is weak.

Their grammar   (grammar knowledge)   knowledge is   is weak

a Bodyguards are paid danger money.

Bodyguards are   are paid   paid danger   danger money

b My cousin Rachel plays rugby.

My cousin   cousin Rachel   Rachel plays   plays rugby

c I like reading detective stories.

I like   like reading   reading detective   detective stories

d This device also measures pressure.

This device   device also   also measures   measures pressure

4 marks

3 Find the four-letter word hidden across two or more consecutive words. Underline the word and write it on the line.

For example: It is as narro<u>w as p</u>ossible.   _____wasp_____

a We can go for our walk now.   _____

b His voice was disguised to conceal his identity.   _____

c The bathroom is tiled from floor to ceiling.   _____

d I would like to be a rodeo rider.   _____

4 marks

Time to reflect

Mark your test out of 12. How did you do?

Check your answers in the back of the book. If any of your answers are incorrect, go to practice section 15 in Practice Book 2 to revise this topic.

30 Analogies

In analogy questions, you need to spot logical links between the words. The link might be the meaning, word structure, spelling or pronunciation.

1   Find the link between the first pair of words and select a word from the list that has the same link. Write the word on the line.

For example: Love is to adore as hate is to ___*despise*___ .

dislike   like   care   annoy   despise

a   Fish are to shoal as bees are to _____ .

hive   flock   fly   swarm   sting

b   Army is to general as navy is to _____ .

admiral   major   ship   exact   specific

c   Devil is to lived as lever is to _____ .

level   reveal   levelled   leaver   revel

d   Coal is to coral as beet is to _____ .

ground   beret   sugar   root   drum

e   Cat is to feline as dog is to _____ .

puppy   poodle   canine   kennel   bark

2   Underline **one** word in **each** set of brackets to complete the sentence in the most sensible way.

For example: Knee is to (ankle, <u>leg</u>, shin) as elbow is to (bone, bend, <u>arm</u>).

a   Time is to (first, second, third) as distance is to (gram, litre, metre).

b   Star is to (sort, rats, sky) as slap is to (lapse, pals, hit).

c   Tea is to (leaves, pot, cup) as coffee is to (hot, black, beans).

d   Train is to (carriage, platform, station) as aeroplane is to (airport, airline, hangar).

e   Key is to (open, ring, quay) as kernel is to (centre, nut, colonel).

f   Word is to (spell, letters, dictionary) as sentence is to (words, verbs, write).

g   Kind is to (sort, cruel, hearted) as plain is to (pattern, prairie, flat).

h   Lead is to (guide, metal, pipe) as bass is to (fish, jazz, soprano).

i   Tennis is to (ball, court, sport) as football is to (pitch, green, goal).

j   Dearth is to (lack, end, lifeless) as flaw is to (carpet, defect, floor).

5 marks

10 marks

Time to reflect

Mark your test out of 15. How did you do?

Check your answers in the back of the book. If any of your answers are incorrect, go to practice section 16 in Practice Book 1 to revise this topic.

31 Close reading

These questions test your ability to think logically, and to work methodically and systematically through a series of statements or facts.

For example:

Jennifer met her friend at 12.15pm. The walk to the café took them 13 minutes. They spent 35 minutes in the café and 12 minutes in the stationery shop next door. They spent 7 minutes chatting outside, then realised they were nearly late to meet Jennifer's mum so they ran to the car park which took them 3 minutes.

What was the time when Jennifer and her friend met Jennifer's mum at the car park?

_____ 1.25pm _____

1 Alfie, Ella, Josh and Ruby all live in the same, five-storey block of flats. None of them lives on the ground or second floors. Ella and Ruby live next door to each other. Alfie doesn't have as many stairs to climb to get to his flat as the others do. Josh lives in the flat directly underneath Ella's.

   a On which floor does Alfie live?

   _____

   b On which floor do Ella and Ruby live?

   _____

   c On which floor does Josh live?

   _____

3 marks

2 Samir's birthday is 3rd January. His friend Luke was born ten days before Samir, and two days before their classmate Leah.

   When is Leah's birthday?

   _____

1 mark

3 Oliver is standing in the school playground. There are buildings on each corner of it, forming the points of a square. In one corner is the science lab, which is to the west of Oliver's form room. His form room is to the north-east of the music room. The music room is to the west of the cloakroom.

   a In which direction does Oliver walk in the morning after he hangs up his coat and makes his way to his form room for registration?

   _____

   b His first lesson is music. In which direction does Oliver walk to get there after registration?

   _____

2 marks

10

4   Three friends ran a marathon. Lucy was the fastest: her time was 3 hours 10 minutes. Jay finished the race exactly an hour later than Lucy. Jess ran faster than Jay and finished half an hour before him. The race starting pistol went off at 10.00 am.

At what time did Jess reach the finishing line?

_____

1
mark

5   Daniel, Asha, Chloe and Zane all took part in at least one of the activities offered at the beach holiday club. The activities on offer were windsurfing, water polo, beach volleyball and sailing. Asha and Daniel went sailing nearly every morning. Asha was back again in the sea each afternoon, this time windsurfing. Zane doesn't like any watersports. Daniel and Chloe played water polo, but, out of the two of them, only Chloe played beach volleyball.

a   Which activities did Daniel do?

_____

b   Who played beach volleyball?

_____

c   How many children went windsurfing?

_____

3
marks

Time to reflect

Mark your test out of 10. How did you do?

Check your answers in the back of the book. If any of your answers are incorrect, go to practice section 17 in Practice Book 1 to revise this topic.

32 Word logic

You will need to read the text and questions carefully here and use logic to make deductions. Unlike for other tests and topics, your own knowledge is irrelevant here – the answer must be found in the text.

(10)

For example:

Read the information below then answer the question that follows.

Gold earrings are expensive. Mollie is wearing large gold earrings.

Tick the sentence below that must be true.

- [ ] Mollie has a lot of money.
- [✓] Mollie's earrings were expensive.
- [ ] Small earrings are cheaper than large ones.
- [ ] Large earrings cost a lot of money.

1 Read the information below then answer the question that follows.

Deciduous trees shed their leaves annually. Oaks and sycamores are deciduous trees.

Tick the sentence below that must be true.

- [ ] All deciduous trees have leaves.
- [ ] The leaves of oak trees fall off in autumn.
- [ ] All trees that shed their leaves are deciduous.
- [ ] Sycamores shed their leaves each year.

1 mark

2 Read the information below then answer the question that follows.

Reuben and Elsie are in Mrs. Khan's class. Every child in Mrs. Khan's class plays the violin.
All violinists love classical music.

Tick the sentence below that must be true.

- [ ] Mrs. Khan plays the violin.
- [ ] Elsie loves classical music.
- [ ] All classical musicians play the violin.
- [ ] Reuben cannot play the violin.

1 mark

3   Read the information below then answer the question that follows.

In my town, the speed limit of roads that have street lights is 30 miles per hour. The speed limit of roads without street lights is 40 miles per hour. However, any road where a school is located is subject to a maximum speed limit of 20 miles per hour, regardless of whether there are street lights or not. I live in Chestnut Avenue, and go to St. Martin's School in Station Road.

Tick the sentence below that cannot be true.

☐   Chestnut Avenue has street lights.

☐   The speed limit on School Lane is 30 miles per hour.

☐   The speed limit on the outskirts of town is 40 miles per hour.

☐   The speed limit on Station Road is 20 miles per hour.

1 mark

4   Read the information below then answer the question that follows.

Felix is Charlie's son and Theo's twin. Linda is Theo's mother and Sally's daughter.

Tick the sentence below that must be true.

☐   Linda is Felix's mother.

☐   Sally is Charlie's grandmother.

☐   Charlie is Linda's brother.

☐   Linda has no daughters.

1 mark

Time to reflect

Mark your test out of 4. How did you do?

Check your answers in the back of the book. If any of your answers are incorrect, go to practice section 15 in Practice Book 2 to revise this topic.

33 Riddles

These questions require you to use your skills of logic and deduction to solve the riddle. Compare the letters in words to work out which are relevant and which are not.

(10)

For example:

Solve the riddle. Write your answer on the line.

My first is in HOUSE but not in MOUSE.

My second is in ROAR but not in SURE.

My third is in SCARF but not in HALF.

My fourth is in HOSE but not in DOZE.

My last is not in FAIR but is in FARE.

The word is: _____HORSE_____

---

1 Solve the riddle. Write your answer on the line.

My first is in DIVE but not in DICE.

My second is in PORT but not in PART.

My third is in FIVE, SIX and EIGHT.

My fourth is in CHEESE but not in PLEASE.

My last is not in TAIL but is in TALE.

The word is: _____

1 mark

---

2 Solve the riddle. Write your answer on the line.

My first is in TABLE but not in FEAST.

My second is in ROVER but not in RIVER.

My third is in SUGAR but not in SYRUP.

My fourth is in MUG and also in CUP.

My last is in MOST and is in COAST.

The word is: _____

1 mark

3 Solve the riddle. Write your answer on the line.

My first is in CANE but not in LANE.

My second is in ITALY and also in SPAIN.

My third is in BARK but not in BIKE.

My fourth is in TRICK but not in TRIKE.

My fifth is in BUTTER but not in BREAD.

My last is in THROWS and also in INSTEAD.

The word is: _____

1
mark

4 Solve the riddle. Write your answer on the line.

My first is in RESPONSE but not in DIVERSION.

My second is in both GUFFAW and CHUCKLE.

My third is in RUBBISH but not in HILARIOUS.

My fourth is in WILDERNESS but not in WEIRDNESS.

My fifth is in INOCULATE but not in NOCTURNAL.

My last is in MACARONI but not in MINORITY.

The word is: _____

1
mark

Time to reflect

Mark your test out of 4. How did you do?

Check your answers in the back of the book. If any of your answers are incorrect, go to practice section 16 in Practice Book 2 to revise this topic.

34 Problem solving

These problems require you to think logically and work systematically to organise and extract the information you need.

For example:

Complete the grid so that all six words can be found either vertically or horizontally.

One word has been included.

THE   ARM   ~~EEL~~   TEA   ELM   HER

T	H	E
E	E	L
A	R	M

1   Read the information and use it to complete the diagram.

Six friends – Archie, Jack, Dylan, Millie, Orla and Ella – went to the theatre. Millie sat between two of her friends. Archie sat directly behind Jack. Orla had Jack on one side of her, and her sister on the other. Dylan sat in seat B1.

Fill in the correct person in the correct seat.

S T A G E

A1	A2	A3
B1	B2	B3

1 mark

2   Complete the grid so that all six words can be found either vertically or horizontally. One word has been included.

~~AGO~~   EGO   JAB   BOY   JET   TOY

A	G	O

1 mark

3   Read the information and use it to complete the diagram.

A box of chocolates contains eight different varieties. All three one-word varieties are in the same row. The strawberry cream is at the far left of the top row, next to the almond crunch. The fudge is at the far right of a row. The butterscotch is opposite the strawberry cream and next to the coffee truffle. The salted caramel is opposite the nougat. The Turkish delight is in the remaining spot.

Fill in the correct chocolate in the correct place.

1	2	3	4
5	6	7	8

1 mark

4   Read the information and use it to complete the diagram.

Liam arrived late at the swimming pool, and there was just one empty locker left. Zachary, Oscar and Lacey had each chosen an even-numbered locker. Oscar's locker was between Charlotte's locker and Mia's. Zachary's locker was at the end of the row, on the right. Lacey had put her things in the locker below Charlotte's.

Fill in the correct person in the correct locker.

1	2	3
4	5	6

1 mark

5   Complete the grid so that all six words can be found on the grid either vertically or horizontally. One word has been included.

ANY   ERA   SUM   MAY   SEA   ~~URN~~

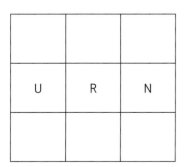

1 mark

Time to reflect

Mark your test out of 5. How did you do?

Check your answers in the back of the book. If any of your answers are incorrect, go to practice section 17 in Practice Book 2 to revise this topic.

Notes

Answers

Vocabulary building

1 Combining words

1 **a** <u>any</u>, <u>way</u>

    b <u>cap</u>, <u>size</u>

    c <u>bud</u>, <u>get</u>

    d <u>ant</u>, <u>hem</u>

2 rein → force (reinforce)

    head → long (headlong)

    foot → print (footprint)

    broad → sheet (broadsheet)

3 **a** water

    b air

    c night

4 **a** may<u>hem</u>

    b sun<u>dry</u>

    c dam<u>son</u>

2 Homophones

1 **a** cymbals

    b quay

    c stationary

    d practise

2 **a** <u>minor</u>

    b <u>weigh</u>

    c <u>raze</u>

3 Dad and I went to the supermarket to (bye) food for tonight's meal. We bought some (flower) to make pizza (doe), two (chilly) peppers, some green beans and a few mushrooms. We walked up and down all of the (isles) looking for tomato (source).

---

b If you chose 'ten' instead of 'size', or 'high' instead of 'cap', revise the spellings of 'captain' and 'heighten'.

c If you chose 'dig' instead of 'bud' learn the spelling of 'digit'.

d Remember that 't' changes its sound when it combines with an 'h'.

'Re-' is a common prefix. Look out for this when you have a short word starting with 're-', like 'rein'. When 're-' is a prefix, it is always pronounced 'ree'; the 'e' doesn't combine with the following vowel.

---

a Watercolour, waterfall, watermelon, watertight

b Airfield, airline, airlock, airstrip

c Nightcap, nightfall, nightgown, nightmare

If you didn't know the word 'sundry', look it up in a dictionary. Note the pronunciation of 'dry' in this word.

Remember that 's' can be pronounced as 'z'.

If you are unfamiliar with any words used in this section, or are unsure why an answer is correct, look up the meaning in a dictionary. Make a note of any new words you come across.

It may be possible to 'raise' a building – but, when explosives are mentioned, the answer must be 'raze'. This has the opposite meaning.

The correct spellings are 'buy', 'flour', 'dough', 'chilli', 'aisles', and 'sauce'.

4 **a** review   principal

    b peel   grate

    c base   sheer

    d pier   tide

'Princi**pal**' is an adjective, meaning 'main or most important'. 'Princi**ple**' is a noun, meaning 'general truth or rule'.

3 Move a letter

1 **a** (r)

    b (m)

    c (b)

The new words are:
a bead, streak
b clap, cremate
c read, sable

2 **a** deter

    b meteor

    c sceptic

a deer + t
b meter + o
c septic + c

3 **a** haven, freight

    b cater, bungle

    c pear, slight

4 **a** b

    b i

    c e

The new words are:
a rush, garbage
b sold, genie
c blow, grime

4 Common letters

1 **a** o: opal, olive, omen, orange, odour

    b s: sadder, shovel, slime, strain, stripe

When you think you have identified the correct letter, check it goes before all of the words in the list. The letter 'a' goes before two words in **a** but is not the right answer.

2 **a** o: hero, veto, cameo, lasso, rodeo

    b e: bide, cube, made, plume, shine

Remember that pronunciation of the word might change when a letter is added, as in the case of 'cameo'.

3 **a** w: straw, wheat

    b u: menu, unit

    c a: china, aisle

When the word 'China' refers to the country, it is a proper noun and is spelled with a capital 'C'. But 'china' spelled with a small 'c' is a common noun and refers to cups and plates, or to the material that makes them.

4 **a** l: level, larch, scowl, lodge

    b y: belly, yeast, decay, yearn

    c s: hiss, sweat, news, sprite

5 **a** go: cargo, goose

    b pe: grape, perch

    c re: adore, realm

The letter combination 'rch' contains no vowels, so the letter that's before this group must be a vowel.

5 Groups of words

1 a <u>verb</u>

   b <u>yogurt</u>

   c <u>ruby</u>

   d <u>sphere</u>

> a The link is that the words are all parts of speech.
> b Yogurt is a dairy product, the same as the group above.
> c All these words are types of gemstones.
> d These words are all 3D shapes.

2 a <u>ring</u>

   b <u>break</u>

   c <u>present</u>

   d <u>pen</u>

> 'Pen' is also the name for an enclosure for farm animals.

   e <u>book</u>

3 a <u>bear</u>

   b <u>fair</u>

   c <u>refuse</u>

> Remember that different meaning of words can have different pronunciations.

   d <u>object</u>

> Sometimes the different pronunciation is due to a different syllable being stressed.

   e <u>jam</u>

6 Words most similar

1 a <u>tired</u>, <u>drowsy</u>

   b <u>high</u>, <u>tall</u>

   c <u>hobby</u>, <u>pastime</u>

   d <u>watch</u>, <u>observe</u>

   e <u>right</u>, <u>correct</u>

> Remember that 'right' has several meanings.

   f <u>pine</u>, <u>long</u>

> As well as being a tree, 'pine' is also a verb meaning to yearn or to long eagerly. 'Long' is also a verb, as well as an adjective.

2 a <u>dwell</u>

   b <u>loathe</u>

   c <u>cheat</u>

   d <u>conceited</u>

> If you are 'vain' or 'conceited' you like looking at yourself in the mirror.

   e <u>dignified</u>

> 'State' and 'nation' are synonyms, but the adjectives 'stately' and 'national' have developed separate meanings.

3 a <u>absurd</u>

   b <u>duplicate</u>

> About half of all words that end in -te end in -ate.

   c <u>fearful</u>

   d <u>require</u>

> Over 80% of all words that end in -ul end in -ful.

   e <u>nauseous</u>

7 Words most opposite

1   **a**   <u>uniform</u>, <u>varied</u> •———————————

> The adjective 'uniform' means the same or unchanging.

     b   <u>plain</u>, <u>fancy</u>

     c   <u>raise</u>, <u>lower</u>

     d   <u>solid</u>, <u>flimsy</u>

     e   <u>wild</u>, <u>tame</u>

     f   <u>lawful</u>, <u>illegal</u>

2   **a**   <u>insolent</u> •———————————

> Make sure you read the words carefully. 'Impudent' means rude and is an antonym of 'polite', but here the word is 'imprudent', with an added 'r'. This word means foolish or impulsive.

     b   <u>barren</u>

     c   <u>sophisticated</u>

     d   <u>victor</u>

     e   <u>leave</u> •———————————

> 'Arrive' and 'depart' are opposites, as are 'arrival' and 'departure', but the two sets can't be mixed.

3   **a**   <u>virtue</u>

     b   <u>guest</u>

     c   <u>unsure</u>

     d   <u>brief</u>

     e   <u>follow</u>

8 Antonyms and synonyms

1   **a**   needy, destitute •———————————

> Choose options that are the same word class. In **a**, 'poverty' is incorrect because it is a noun whereas 'wealthy' is an adjective.

     b   dice, cut

     c   exterior

     d   overdue, late

     e   sack, dismiss •———————————

> 'Fire' can be used as a verb or a noun. Here, the verb is used.

2   **a**   amend, adjust •———————————

> 'Alter', spelled -er, is a synonym of 'change'. 'Altar', spelled -ar, is an area of a church.

     b   seldom, rarely

     c   stumble

     d   meagre •———————————

> 'Meagre' means lacking in quantity.

     e   unreal, imaginary

9 Anagrams

1
  a TREACLE

  b CURTAIN

  c TEACHER

  d RESPONSE

2
  a DOLPHIN

  b POETRY

  c AUCTION ●————— CAUTION is also an anagram of OTINUCA, but it is not a sale where buyers make bids.

  d SCORPION

  e MERINGUE ●————— Be careful of your spelling of this word.

3
  a <u>TRIVIA</u>

  b <u>LOSER</u>, <u>STOLEN</u>

  c <u>THINNER</u>

  d <u>HEARTH</u>, <u>RATHER</u>

  e <u>FLAME</u>

Words in context

10 Odd words out

1
  a <u>amber</u>, <u>pineapple</u>

  b <u>oil</u>, <u>gas</u>

  c <u>ewe</u>, <u>arc</u>

  d <u>timer</u>, <u>dial</u>

a The other words are all names of citrus fruits.
b The other words are all names of metals.
c The other words are all names for trees. Look out for homophones: 'ewe' sounds the same as 'yew', which is a tree, but a 'ewe' is a sheep.
d The other words are verbs meaning 'see' or 'view'.

2
  a (brash)

  b (common)

  c (second)

  d (stone)

a 'Brash' means over-confident.
b The other words are all names of army ranks.
c The other words mean 'very small'. 'Minute' is pronounced 'my-newt' here.
d The other words are names for currencies.

3
  a sequel

  b class

  c trainer

  d leveret ●————— A 'leveret' is a young hare.

4
  a <u>line</u>, <u>stroll</u>

  b <u>present</u>, <u>shine</u>

  c <u>duck</u>, <u>eel</u>

11 Jumbled sentences

1 **a** Babysitters look <u>for</u> children <u>after</u> money.

    b It's only a <u>loud</u> dog, but it has a <u>small</u> bark.

> 'Only' usually has a negative meaning, so is more likely to describe a small thing than a big one.

    c I'd like to go <u>see</u> Egypt to <u>to</u> the Pyramids.

> Make sure to underline the right 'to'.

    d My mum feels <u>boring</u> at work because her job is so <u>frustrated.</u>

    e I heard the lion <u>raw</u> when the keeper gave it some <u>roar</u> meat.

> Beware of homophones; 'raw' and 'roar' sound the same, so when you read the sentence out loud, it sounds fine.

2 **a** What a fantastic match it was!

> 'What' is not only a question word. When it is used to introduce an exclamation, the subject pronoun and verb are not inverted.

    b She was dressed in a long, cotton nightgown.

> 'Cotton long nightgown' is wrong. If you are not sure why, revise the rules regarding the order of adjectives.

    c You'd better go now, or you'll miss your train.

    d I would rather you went home.

3 **a** (theirs)

> Remember, only one word is not needed.

      The station is nearer their house than ours.
      / Their house is nearer the station than ours.

    b (letter)

      I've written to all my cousins.

    c (very)

      Is there enough time for me to have a shower?

12 Word meanings

1 **a** <u>keep</u>

> If you got any of these questions wrong, look up the words in a dictionary.

    b <u>varied</u>

> Look for words in the sentence that give you clues. Here, the word 'ranging' suggests a wide variety.

    c <u>limited</u>

    d <u>rickety</u>

2 compassion → deep sympathy

    restructure → organise differently

    novice → beginner

    chronometer → device for measuring time

    atypical → not representative

3 **a** Saturn's moon might <u>harbour</u> an underground ocean beneath its icy surface.

> 'Harbour' is a verb, as well as a noun.

    b He is totally charmless, and few people are <u>gullible</u> enough to believe his superficial and glib words.

> Use your knowledge of suffixes: words ending '-ful' or '-ible' are adjectives, so you should underline an adjective in the sentence.

c Her candid and <u>uncompromising</u> attitude often annoyed her boss, who was more genial and relaxed.

d The children scared their amiable parents by peering through their elaborate, <u>grotesque</u> masks.

Adjectives that are linked by 'and' are often related in meaning, so if you knew that 'relaxed' was a positive description, you could assume that 'genial' was positive, too. The word 'inflexible' is negative when describing a person.

13 Word analogies

1 a REIN

b COPE

c SANDY

d FORM

e CLOCK

f TIER

g LENT

h PALE

i HALL

j SPAN

k LIGHTNING

l LAST

The pattern is:
a change the second letter to 'E'
b remove the fourth letter
c replace the first letter with 'S'
d 1324
e replace the first letter with the fourth letter
f remove the third letter
g remove the first and last letters
h 1325, with the fourth letter deleted
i put 'H' before the first three letters
j 4123
k things that go in pairs
l words that are opposites.

2 a B

b E

A mule is a backless shoe as well as an animal.

c C

d A

A vault is an underground chamber as well as a verb meaning to jump.

14 Words in context

1 a <u>horse</u>, <u>galloped</u>

b <u>kind</u>, <u>helping</u>

'Quickly' is a clue that galloped, not walked, is meant.

c <u>detour</u>, <u>avoid</u>

d <u>sizzled</u>, <u>smelled</u>

'Reeked' means 'smelled awful'.

e <u>bequeathed</u>, <u>will</u>

Don't confuse 'testament', another word for 'will', with 'testimony', which means proof.

f <u>bicycle</u>, <u>puncture</u>

g <u>remind</u>, <u>post</u>, <u>forget</u>

h <u>seats</u>, <u>audience</u>, <u>stand</u>

i <u>many</u>, <u>spoilt</u>, <u>appetite</u>

j <u>tenants</u>, <u>notice</u>, <u>vacated</u>

k <u>income</u>, <u>large</u>, <u>credit</u>

l <u>cruise</u>, <u>overboard</u>, <u>drowned</u>

2 **a** ~~night~~ → dawn

    b ~~hear~~ → make

    c ~~sticks~~ → needles

    d ~~bland~~ → hot/spicy

    e ~~cage~~ → nest

15 Complete the sentence

1 **a** cel<u>eb</u>rate

    b ho<u>ve</u>red •————— The verb is clearly in the past tense because it ends in -d, so the letter before is almost certainly 'e'.

    c outr<u>ageou</u>s

    d <u>ou</u>tr<u>u</u>n

    e Atte<u>ndan</u>ce •————— About half of all words that end in -ce end in -nce, so it is always worth trying to see if writing an 'n' helps.

    f he<u>alth</u>y

2 **a** down

    b even

    c as

    d laid •————— Be careful of the two verbs 'lie' and 'lay'. The past tense of 'lie' is 'lay', and the past participle is 'lain'. The past tense and past participle of 'lay' are both 'laid'. The present tense of this sentence would be 'Mum lays the baby in her cot and tiptoes away'.

    e increasingly

    f in

3 **a** <u>decision</u> •————— You deliver or reach a verdict, not make one.

    b <u>tell</u> •————— 'Advice' is a noun; 'advise' is the corresponding verb.

    c <u>so</u>

    d <u>strongly</u>

    e <u>postpone</u>

    f <u>stroll</u> •————— 'Stroll' is the only word here which goes with 'leisurely'.

16 Complete the paragraph

1 <u>crew</u>, <u>area</u>, <u>trace</u>, <u>claim</u>, <u>mythical</u>, <u>meteorologists</u>, <u>current</u>, <u>route</u>, <u>incident</u> •————— The sentence goes on to talk about hurricanes, and meteorologists are people who study and forecast the weather.

2 long, never, gridlocked, congestion, standstill, high, heavy, often, discourages

Numbers

17 Completing equations

1 **a** 7

You can check your answers in exercises like this by calculating both sides of the calculation. If your answer is correct, both sides will match.

    b 2

    c 7

    d 2

2 **a** 8

    b 7

    c 9

    d 240

If you made a mistake in this exercise, you may not have followed the correct order of operations. Multiply and divide numbers first, before you add and subtract.

3 **a** 17

    b 29

    c 6

    d 5

    e 152

    f 19

    g 35

    h 60

18 Number analogies

1 **a** 20

    b 40

    c 2

You need to divide the number on the left by 12

    d 144

You need to square the number on the left.

2 **a** add the numbers outside the brackets, and then multiply your result by 2

There might be different ways of reaching the bracketed number in the first set. For instance, you could get the answer by multiplying 3 and 4 and adding 2. However, that formula would not give you the right answer in the second set of numbers. Make sure you work out both sets.

    b divide the first number by 4

    c square the number on the left, and add the number on the right.

3 **a** ③

    b ㊌

    c ⑳

    d ⑬⓪

a Divide the first number by the second.
b Multiply the two numbers, and then double the answer.
c Add the two numbers, and then add 3
d Add the two numbers, then add 10

4
 a 8

 b 35

 c 39

 d 12

a Add the two numbers, and then divide the answer by 2

b Add the two numbers, and then subtract 3

c Multiply the two numbers, and then add 9

d Double the second number and add it to the first number.

19 Algebra

1
 a E

 b D

 c A

 d C

Remember to do the calculation in brackets first.

2
 a 17

 b 31

 c 21

 d 27

3
 a 15

 b 1

 c 24

 d 18

4
 a B

 b D

 c D

 d C

20 Number triples

1
 a 2

 b 46

 c 128

 d 11

 e 44

 f 21

 g 18

 h 6

The relationship is:

a divide the left-hand number by the right-hand number

b add both outside numbers together, then multiply the result by 2

c multiply the two outside numbers

d multiply the left-hand number by 2, then add the right-hand number to the result

e multiply the two outside numbers, then subtract 10 from the result

f subtract the left-hand number from the right-hand number, then add 2

g subtract 1 from each of the outside numbers, then multiply those numbers

h divide the left-hand number by the right-hand number, then subtract 1 from the result.

2

a 19.5

b 81

c 0.95

d 20

e 143

f 5

g 29

h 4

The relationship is:
a add 2.5 to the left-hand number
b square the left-hand number
c divide the left-hand number by 2
d multiply the left-hand number by 5, then add 10 to the result
e multiply the left-hand number by 11
f cube the number on the right; the left-hand number is the cube root of the number on the right
g multiply the left-hand number by 3, then add 2
h subtract 1 from the left-hand number, then divide by 2

Sequences and codes

21 Letter sequences

1

a M, R

b K, E

c V, Y

d F, Q

2

a JD

b IR

c UU

d GV

3

a VW, XY

b ON, ML

c WI, ZK

d VW, EF

e RJ, NN

4

a G, I

b K, H

c UQ, WO

d HG, FH

If you don't spot an obvious sequence through all the numbers, there might be two separate patterns: one for the odd numbers and one for the even numbers.

The two letters that make up each individual pair are not linked in any way: compare the first letters of both pairs, then the second letters. Mark the first sequence above the alphabet and the second sequence below it, so you don't get confused.
a First letter: −1; second letter: −1
b First letter: −4; second letter: +4
c First letter: +1; second letter: −1
d First letter: +3; second letter: −2

a Repeat the letter then omit 1 letter.
b Here there's just one sequence: −3
c First letter: +2; second letter: −2
d First letter: −2; second letter: +1

22 Number sequences

1

a 13, 21

b 16.5, 18

c 382, 766

a Add the two previous numbers.
b +1.5
c ×2 and then +2 each time (or double the amount increased each time: +6, +12, +24, +48…).

d First pattern: +13; alternate pattern: +6
e +2, +4, +6, +8, +10, +12
f ÷3
g ×2 then +2 each time

54, 222

2 a first pattern: ×2; alternate pattern: ÷2

> If you don't spot an obvious sequence through all the numbers, there might be two separate patterns, one for the first, third and fifth numbers, and one for the second, fourth and sixth.

b first pattern: +12; alternate pattern: +15

c −8, −9, −10, −11, −12

d ÷2

e first pattern: −8; alternate pattern: ÷3

f +12, +13, +14, +15, +16

> It is also correct if you have expressed your answers in words. For example: 'The amount being added on increases by 1 each time.'

g +3, +4, +5, +6, +7

3 a ⓹⓹

b ㊼

c ㊵

> **a** Add the two previous numbers.
> **b** +7
> **c** First pattern: −9; alternate pattern: +3

23 Codes and decodes

1 a RKPM

b UZXV

c ATRG

> The code pattern is:
> **a** +2
> **b** a mirror code
> **c** −1

2 a LIMIT

b STORK

c FISH

> The code pattern is:
> **a** −4, so the decode pattern is +4
> **b** −3
> **c** odd letters +1; even letters −1

3 a CAST

b STORE

c CHEAT

> The code pattern is:
> **a** odd letters +1; even letters +2
> **b** −2
> **c** odd letters +3; even letters −1
> **d** +3

4 a XJJVF

b HSGAC

c ETWSHQ

d GLQQHU

> The decode pattern is:
> **a** a mirror code
> **b** −1, −2, −3, −4, −5
> **c** odd letters +2; even letters −1
> **d** a mirror code.

5 a WALTZ

b BEACH

c WINTER

d SPICE

24 Word ladders

1 **a** DRAG

    b SIGH

    c PALM •——————— The vegetable is spelled KALE, not CALE, so PALM is the only option here.

    d SHOP

    e BLOW

    f GLUE

    g PEER

    h COME

    i LICK

    j MEND

2 **a** PART, PANT

    b THIN, SHIN

    c LORD, FORD

    d WAIL, WALL

    e PAIN, RAIN

    f FREE, FLEE

    g FOOD, FOOL

    h RAIL, RAIN

    i WHOLE, WHOSE

    j BRINK, BLINK •——————— Although DRANK is possible as your first change, you get stuck at this point, as BRANK and DLANK are not words. If you reach a dead end like this, start again, this time choosing another letter to change.

25 Word triples

1 **a** TEN

    b PIN

    c RED

    d SOB

    e ELF •——————— Number each letter consecutively (excluding the ones in brackets) to find the pattern.
          a 351
          b 346
          c 156

    f SLIP   **d** 521
          e 254

    g PORT   **f** 1235
          g 1674

    h HELP   **h** 3468
          i 2834

    i OATH

j YEARN

k RULE

l WATER

m CLEAN

n SKIRT

j 10,8,3,1,7
k 2891
l 87645
m 64529
n 49721

26 Codes and decodes

1 **a** 8765

b 9786

c 9665

T = 5, E = 6, O = 7, P = 8, M = 9

2 **a** 3748

b DRINK

c BRAIN

d 3694

D = 2, B = 3, N = 4, I = 5, O = 6, A = 7, K = 8, R = 9

3 **a** 8697

b 5986

c 6795

P = 5, T = 6, R = 7, S = 8, A = 9

Missing letters

27 Missing 3 letters

1 **a** (OUT)

b (BAR)

c (IMP)

d (HEM)

Make sure the word makes sense in the sentence. REACT is a word, but it doesn't fit here.

RIPPLE and TOPPLE are words, but they don't make sense here.

SCARE and SCRAPE are words, but they don't make sense here. Remember, when H follows C, its pronunciation changes.

2 SCA**REC**ROW

PL**AUSI**BLE

CON**SEN**SUS

CONS**CIE**NCE

3 **a** ORE

b LEG

c RAT

The instructions tell you to write 'a word', so the three letters must form a real English word.

4 **a** INI

b ERA

The instructions do not specify that the 3 letters must be a word, so your answer in itself does not have to form a real word.

'Definitely', 'broccoli', and 'professor' are tricky words that a lot of people spell wrong. Make sure you learn them.

c COL

d ESS

28 Missing random letters

1 **a** STUDIOUS

> -ious is a common adjective suffix, so look out for words ending in it.

b LIFEGUARD

c COMMUNAL

> Don't confuse 'communal', spelled with a 'u', with the word 'common'.

d THROUGHOUT

e FACTUAL

2 Conkers is a tra**diti**onal children's game played with the hard, shiny seeds of horse c**hes**t**nu**t trees. Two players each use a conker t**hrea**ded on to a length of string, and the aim of the game is to smash the other player's conker to bits. Adults play, too, and there are even co**mpet**itions and a world championship. These are always held in **au**t**umn**, which is when conkers are available. Participants are supplied with ready-strung conkers – they are not **all**owed to use their own, in case they have baked them or soaked them in vinegar to harden the conker and so obtain an unfair ad**vant**age over their op**po**ne**nt**. The best conkers last se**vera**l seasons and may even be passed down from older to younger s**ibling**s.

3 **a** FUGI̱TI̱VE

b AGG̱RES̱SIVE

c COṈTRADI̱CT

d DE̱VO̱TION

e DISI̱ṈTEG̱RATE

f PEṞPEṮUAL

Logic

29 Hidden words

1 **a** brid**ge ne**eded, gene

b Th**e el**ephant, heel

c pyja**mas s**hrank, mass

d co**ach e**xcursion, ache

2 **a** (danger money)

> The hidden word is:
> **a** germ
> **b** help
> **c** vest
> **d** some

b (Rachel plays)

c (detective stories)

d (also measures)

3 **a** walk <u>now</u>, know

    b hi<u>s ide</u>ntity, side

    c bathroo<u>m is ti</u>led, mist

    d <u>be a r</u>odeo, bear

> Spelling is important in this sort of question. If you didn't know the correct spelling of 'roar' you might have underlined 'f<u>or our</u>'.

30 Analogies

1 **a** swarm

    b admiral

    c revel

    d beret

    e canine

> **c** The link is that each word is written backwards.
>
> **d** The letter 'r' is inserted in the middle of each word.

2 **a** <u>second</u>, <u>metre</u>

    b <u>rats</u>, <u>pals</u>

    c <u>leaves</u>, <u>beans</u>

    d <u>station</u>, <u>airport</u>

    e <u>quay</u>, <u>colonel</u>

    f <u>letters</u>, <u>words</u>

    g <u>cruel</u>, <u>pattern</u>

    h <u>metal</u>, <u>fish</u>

    i <u>court</u>, <u>pitch</u>

    j <u>lack</u>, <u>defect</u>

> **b** Each word is written backwards.
> **e** The link is that the words are homophones: they are pronounced in the same way.
> **f** Words are made up of letters, and sentences are made up of words.
> **g** These are opposites.
> **h** Look out for words that have several pronunciations.
> **j** If you didn't know the meanings of 'dearth' and 'flaw', look them up. The link is that the words are synonyms.

31 Close reading

1 **a** First floor

    b Fourth floor

    c Third floor

2 26th December

3 **a** North

    b South-west

4 Twenty to two / 1.40 pm

5 **a** Sailing and water polo

    b Zane and Chloe

    c One

> Alfie doesn't have as many stairs to climb, so the others live on higher floors.

> If no-one lives on the second floor, Josh cannot live on the first floor. He cannot live on the fourth floor, as this is the top floor. Remember to count the ground floor in the five-storey block of flats.

> Luke was born ten days earlier than Samir, which is 24th December. This is two days before Leah's birthday.

> If you got this wrong, try drawing a map to get the right answer.

> Jay's time was 4 hours 10 minutes. Jess's time was 3 hours 40 minutes, so she finished 3 hours and 40 minutes after 10.00 am.

32 Word logic

1 Sycamores shed their leaves each year.

2 Elsie loves classical music.

3 The speed limit on Station Road is 20 miles per hour.

> We know that there is a school in Station Road, so the speed limit there must be 20 miles per hour or less.

4 Linda is Felix's mother.

33 Riddles

1 VOICE

2 BOGUS

3 CIRCUS

> Learn the spellings of carcass (carcase is also correct) and circuit, if you wrote carcus or circut.

4 PUBLIC

34 Problem solving

1

STAGE

A1 Ella	A2 Orla	A3 Jack
B1 Dylan	B2 Millie	B3 Archie

2

J	E	T
A	G	O
B	O	Y

3

1 Strawberry cream	2 Almond crunch	3 Salted caramel	4 Turkish delight
5 Butterscotch	6 Coffee truffle	7 Nougat	8 Fudge

> Begin with the strawberry cream. The almond crunch is next to it, and they are both two-word varieties. The fudge, nougat and butterscotch must be in the bottom row.

4

1 Charlotte	2 Oscar	3 Mia
4 Lacey	5 Liam	6 Zachary

> Oscar's locker must be number 2, because it is the only even-numbered locker between two others.

5

S	E	A
U	R	N
M	A	Y

Published by Pearson Education Limited, 80 Strand, London, WC2R 0RL.

www.pearsonschools.co.uk

Text © Pearson Education Limited 2018
Edited, typeset and produced by Elektra Media Ltd
Original illustrations © Pearson Education Limited
Illustrated by Elektra Media Ltd
Cover illustration by Lukas Bischoff

The right of Susan Purcell to be identified as author of this work has been asserted by her in accordance with the Copyright, Designs and Patents Act 1988.

First published 2018

21 20 19 18
10 9 8 7 6 5 4 3 2 1

British Library Cataloguing in Publication Data
A catalogue record for this book is available from the British Library

ISBN: 978 1 292 24673 4

Printed in Italy by L.E.G.O. S.p.A.

Acknowledgements
We would like to thank Hannah Hirst-Dunton, Jane Cotter and Graeme Booth for their invaluable help in the development and trialling of this publication.

Note from the publisher
Pearson has robust editorial processes, including answer and fact checks, to ensure the accuracy of the content in this publication, and every effort is made to ensure this publication is free of errors. We are, however, only human, and occasionally errors do occur. Pearson is not liable for any misunderstandings that arise as a result of errors in this publication, but it is our priority to ensure that the content is accurate. If you spot an error, please do contact us at resourcescorrections@pearson.com so we can make sure it is corrected.